# The Weekend Organist

## Service Music for Manuals

### Colin Mawby

Kevin Mayhew

We hope you enjoy the music in *The Weekend Organist.*
Further copies of this and our many other books are available
from your local music shop or Christian bookshop.

In case of difficulty, please contact the publisher direct by writing to:

The Sales Department
KEVIN MAYHEW LTD
Rattlesden
Bury St Edmunds
Suffolk IP30 0SZ

Phone 01449 737978
Fax 01449 737834

Please ask for our complete catalogue of outstanding Church Music.

Front Cover: Photograph of St Lawrence Church, Stanmore, London
by Derek Forss.  Reproduced by kind permission.

Cover designed by Jaquetta Sergeant.

First published in Great Britain in 1997 by Kevin Mayhew Ltd.

ISBN 1 84003 058 5
ISMN M 57004 116 9
Catalogue No: 1400151

1 2 3 4 5 6 7 8 9

Music Editor: Nicola Greengrass
Music setting by Vernon Turner

Printed and bound in Great Britain

# Contents

# Preface

This book, designed for the weekend organist, contains straightforward 'manuals only' music for the Sunday Service.

The longer Fanfares can be used as an introduction to the hymns on special occasions; they may also be played as a greeting for an important visitor, or even to mark the arrival of the ordinary procession. The shorter Fanfares should be sounded to preface the Gospel reading on feast days; they may also be used in the same way as the longer Fanfares.

The Quiet Meditations should accompany the Communion or Quiet Time period. Each contains an optional cut (marked by square brackets) so that it may be tailored in length to suit the particular occasion. These pieces may also be used as quiet voluntaries.

The Processionals and Recessionals are interchangeable and they may be shortened if necessary.

The music in this book may be adapted to suit local circumstances: it is written for the busy weekend organist who, while anxious to contribute to a vibrant weekly liturgy, has little time to undertake systematic and concentrated organ practice.

COLIN MAWBY

# FANFARES

## FANFARE IN C

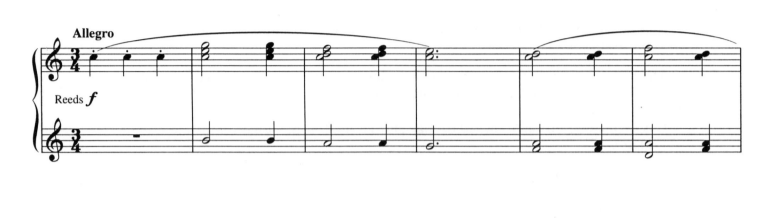

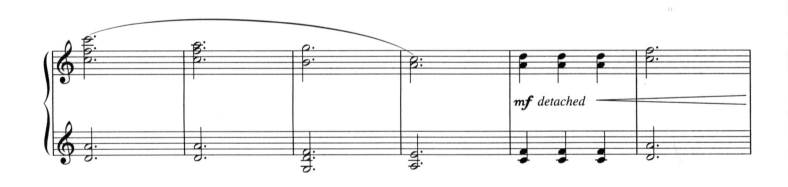

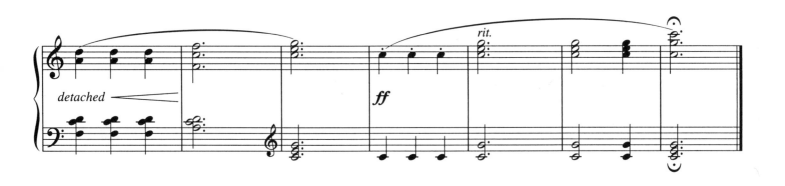

## FANFARE IN G

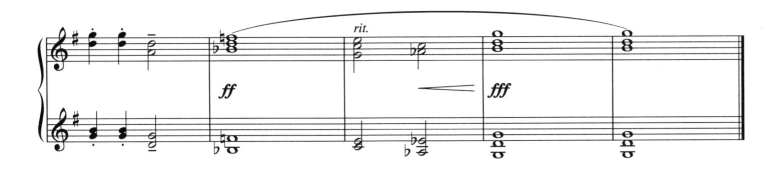

# FANFARE IN D

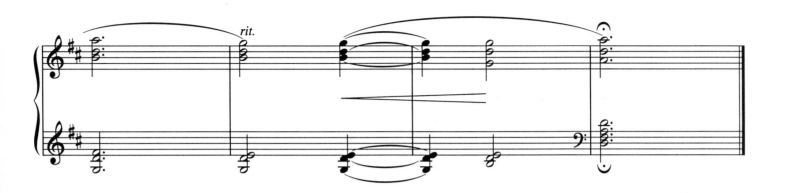

## FANFARE IN A or A♭ *

*This piece may be played in either key, simply by substituting the appropriate key signature.*

## FANFARE IN E or E♭*

*This piece may be played in either key, simply by substituting the appropriate key signature.*

## FANFARE IN F

## FANFARE IN B♭

## SHORT FANFARE IN C

## SHORT FANFARE IN G

## SHORT FANFARE IN D

## SHORT FANFARE IN A or A♭*

*This piece may be played in either key, simply by substituting the appropriate key signature.*

## SHORT FANFARE IN E or E♭*

## SHORT FANFARE IN F

## SHORT FANFARE IN B♭

*\* This piece may be played in either key, simply by substituting the appropriate key signature.*

# PROCESSIONALS

## PROCESSIONAL IN C

# PROCESSIONAL IN G

# PROCESSIONAL IN D

# PROCESSIONAL IN B♭

* If necessary this Processional may end quietly by inserting a diminuendo from this point to the end.

# QUIET PROCESSIONAL IN F

# QUIET PROCESSIONAL IN A

# SHORT PROCESSIONAL IN C

# SHORT PROCESSIONAL IN G

26

## QUIET, SHORT PROCESSIONAL IN F

# QUIET, SHORT PROCESSIONAL IN C

# MEDITATIONS
## QUIET MEDITATION IN A MINOR

# QUIET MEDITATION IN D MINOR

# QUIET MEDITATION IN G MINOR

# QUIET MEDITATION IN E MINOR

# QUIET MEDITATION IN D

# QUIET MEDITATION IN A

# QUIET MEDITATION IN C MINOR

# RECESSIONALS

## RECESSIONAL IN C

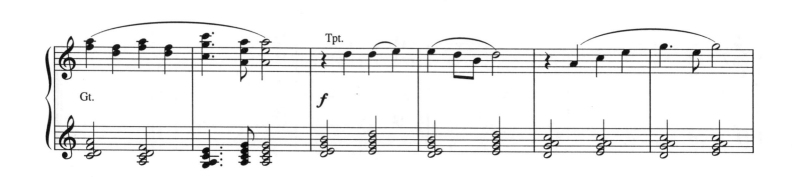

# RECESSIONAL IN G

# RECESSIONAL IN D

47

# RECESSIONAL IN B♭

# RECESSIONAL IN A

51

# QUIET RECESSIONAL IN D MINOR

# SHORT RECESSIONAL IN C

# SHORT RECESSIONAL IN D

## SHORT RECESSIONAL IN E MINOR